rockschool®

Female Vocals
Grade 1

*Performance pieces, technical exercises and in-depth guidance
for Rockschool examinations*

Acknowledgements

Published by Rockschool Ltd. © 2014 under license from Music Sales Ltd.
Catalogue Number RSK091401
ISBN: 978-1-908920-51-5

AUDIO
Backing tracks produced by Music Sales Limited
Supporting test backing tracks recorded by Jon Musgrave, Jon Bishop and Duncan Jordan
Supporting test vocals recorded by Duncan Jordan
Supporting tests mixed at Langlei Studios by Duncan Jordan
Mastered by Duncan Jordan

MUSICIANS
Neal Andrews, Lucie Burns (Lazy Hammock), Jodie Davies,Tenisha Edwards, Noam Lederman,
Beth Loates-Taylor, Dave Marks, Salena Mastroianni, Paul Miro, Ryan Moore, Jon Musgrave,
Chris Smart, Ross Stanley, T-Jay, Stacy Taylor, Daniel Walker

PUBLISHING
Compiled and edited by James Uings, Simon Troup, Stephen Lawson and Stuart Slater
Internal design and layout by Simon and Jennie Troup, Digital Music Art
Cover designed by Philip Millard, Philip Millard Design
Fact Files written by Stephen Lawson, Owen Bailey and Michael Leonard
Additional proofing by Chris Bird, Ronan Macdonald, Jonathan Preiss and Becky Baldwin
Cover photography © Michael Buckner / Getty Images
Full transcriptions by Music Sales Ltd.

SYLLABUS
Vocal specialists: Martin Hibbert and Eva Brandt
Additional consultation: Emily Nash, Stuart Slater and Sarah Page
Supporting tests composition: Martin Hibbert, James Uings, Jon Musgrave, Jodie Davies,
Ryan Moore, Chris Hawkins, Jonathan Preiss
Rhythmic test lyrics: Lucie Burns (Lazy Hammock)

PRINTING
Printed and bound in the United Kingdom by Caligraving Ltd.
Media hosting by Dropcards

DISTRIBUTION
Exclusive Distributors: Music Sales Ltd.

CONTACTING ROCKSCHOOL
www.rockschool.co.uk
Telephone: +44 (0)845 460 4747
Fax: +44 (0)845 460 1960

Table of Contents

Introductions & Information

Page

Rockschool Grade Pieces

Page

Technical Exercises

Page

Supporting Tests

Page

Additional Information

Page

Welcome to Rockschool Female Vocals Grade 1

Welcome to the Rockschool Female Vocals Grade 1 pack. This book and accompanying download card contain everything you need to sing at this grade.

Vocals Exams
At each grade you have the option of taking one of two different types of examination:

- **Grade Exam:** a Grade Exam is a mixture of music performances, technical work and tests. You prepare three pieces (two of which may be Free Choice Pieces) and the contents of the Technical Exercise section. This accounts for 75% of the exam marks. The other 25% consists of: *either* a Sight Reading *or* an Improvisation & Interpretation test (10%), two Ear Tests (10%), and finally you will be asked five General Musicianship Questions (5%). The pass mark is 60%.

- **Performance Certificate:** in a Performance Certificate you sing five pieces. Up to three of these can be Free Choice Pieces. Each song is marked out of 20 and the pass mark is 60%.

Book Contents
The book is divided into a number of sections. These are:

- **Exam Pieces:** in this book you will find six well-known pieces of Grade 1 standard. Each song is preceded by a Fact File detailing information about the original recording, the artist who sang on it and some recommended listening if you wish to research the artist further.

- **Piano and guitar notation:** every exam piece is printed with a piano part and guitar chords. Both are a representation of the overall band arrangement. These have been included to assist you with your practice should you wish to use a piano and/or guitar for accompaniment. In your exam you must perform to the backing tracks provided.

- **Vocal score:** in addition to the piano/vocal/guitar arrangement there is also a separate vocal-only score to allow you to view the vocal part on a single sheet of paper.

- **Technical Exercises:** there are a range of technical exercises in this grade. Some are notated in full, and some give a range of starting notes.

- **Supporting Tests and General Musicianship Questions:** in Vocals Grade 1 there are three supporting tests – *either* a Sight Reading *or* an Improvisation & Interpretation test and two Ear Tests – and a set of General Musicianship Questions (GMQs) asked at the end of each exam. Examples of the types of tests likely to appear in the exam are printed in this book.

- **General Information:** finally, you will find information on exam procedures, including online examination entry, marking schemes, information on Free Choice Pieces and improvisation requirements for each grade.

Audio
Each song in Vocals Grade 1 has an audio track that can be downloaded via the download card that comes with the book. This is a backing track with the vocal taken off so you can sing along with the band. The backing tracks should be used in examinations. There are also audio examples of the supporting tests printed in the book.

The audio files are supplied in MP3 format, the most widely compatible audio format in common usage – MP3s will likely be familiar to anyone with a computer, iPod, smartphone or similar device. Once downloaded you will be able to play them on any compatible device; we hope that you find this extra versatility useful.

Download cards
Download cards are easy to use – simply go to *www.dropcards.com/rsvocals* and type in the code on the back of your card. It's best to do this somewhere with a good connection, to ensure that the download is uninterrupted. If you have any problems with your download, you should be able to resolve them at *www.dropcards.com/help*.

We hope you enjoy using this book. You can find further details about Rockschool's Vocals and other instrumental syllabuses on our website: *www.rockschool.co.uk.*

SONG TITLE: 1234
ALBUM: THE REMINDER
RELEASED: 2007
LABEL: POLYDOR
GENRE: INDIE POP

PERSONNEL: LESLIE FEIST (VOX+BANJO)
BEN MINK (GUITAR)
JULIAN BROWN (BASS)
JESSIE BAIRD (DRUMS)
GONZALES (PIANO)

UK CHART PEAK: 8
US CHART PEAK: 8

BACKGROUND INFO

'1234' was the second single from Feist's third studio album *The Reminder*.

THE BIGGER PICTURE

Leslie Feist was born in Nova Scotia, Canada in 1976. Her father was a painter, and her mother, a student of ceramics. Aged 12, Feist performed as one of 1,000 dancers in the opening ceremony of the Calgary Winter Olympics (she later cited this experience as the inspiration for the video for '1234'). As a child, Feist was interested in becoming a writer and spent much of her time singing in choirs. At the age of 15 she formed her first band, a punk outfit called Placebo (not to be confused with the English rock group of the same name), in which she sang lead vocals. Placebo won a local battle of the bands and were awarded the opening slot at a festival, at which Feist met Brendan Canning who she later joined in the group Broken Social Scene. Her solo career kicked off in 1999 with the release of her debut album, *Monarch (Lay Your Jewelled Head Down)*. Her major label debut, *Let It Die*, followed in 2004. Feist toured for three years, helping the album go platinum in Canada and earning her two Juno Awards for Best New Artist and Best Alternative Rock Album.

NOTES

In 2005, while touring *Let It Die,* Feist was supported by New Buffalo aka Australian singer-songwriter Sally Seltmann. Seltmann had written a song after listening to *Let It Die* and thought it sounded too much like a Feist track to record under her New Buffalo stage name, so she offered it to Feist, who began playing it live and later recorded it as '1234' for her fourth studio album, *The Reminder*. It proved to be her best-selling single. This was in no small part due to a witty choreographed video that went viral on YouTube and the song being used in the TV ads for Apple's iPod Nano. Following the airing of the iPod ad, '1234' went from Number 102 in the UK singles chart to Number 8. In America, the song had been selling 2,000 downloads per week prior to the iPod adverts and ended up shifting over 73,000 total downloads thanks to Apple's use of it.

RECOMMENDED LISTENING

'Mushaboom' featured on Feist's major label debut, *Let It Die*, and was chosen to feature on the soundtrack of the film *500 Days Of Summer*. It has a similarly laid-back sound to '1234'. 'I Feel It All', from *The Reminder*, is more indie rock in flavour and was used in the British TV series *The InBetweeners*.

1234

Feist

Words & Music by Feist & Sally Seltmann

SONG TITLE: GOD BLESS THE CHILD
ALBUM: N/A
RELEASED: 1941
LABEL: OKEH
GENRE: JAZZ

PERSONNEL: BILLIE HOLIDAY (VOX)
ELDDIE HEYWOOD (PIANO)
ROY ELDRIDGE (TRUMPET)
ERNIE POWELL (TRUMPET)
JIMMY POWELL (ALTO SAX)
LESTER BOONE (ALTO SAX)
PAUL CHAPMAN (GUITAR)
GRACHAN MONCUR (BASS)
HERBERT COWANS (DRUMS)

UK CHART PEAK: N/A
US CHART PEAK: N/A

BACKGROUND INFO

'God Bless The Child' is a jazz standard, co-written and recorded by Billie Holiday in 1941.

THE BIGGER PICTURE

Billie Holiday was born Eleanora Fagan in Baltimore in 1915. Her father, jazz guitarist Clarence Holiday, never married Fagan's mother and left when she was a baby. She had a troubled childhood due to her mother not being at home and was sent to a Catholic reform school at the age of 10. Two years later, Fagan and her mother moved to New York for work. Once settled in her new surroundings, Fagan began singing in clubs in Harlem. It was then that she rebranded herself 'Billie Holiday' ('Billie' after an actress she admired called Billie Dove and 'Holiday' after her father). At 18, Holiday made her debut as a recording artist when she cut a single with Benny Goodman. By then she had made a name for herself for her unique singing style: rather than sing a song's melody as written, Holiday would improvise in the way jazz instrumentalists would. Her vocals were also intensely emotional, influenced by Louis Armstrong's vocal style, as Holiday seemed to take a song's lyrics to heart. Holiday later starred with her hero Armstrong in the film *New Orleans* and performed with other jazz artists such as Count Basie, Lester Young (who gave her the title 'Lady Day') and Artie Shaw. But Holiday's personal demons led to her abusing alcohol and drugs, and she died of complications arising from cirrhosis of the liver in 1959.

NOTES

'God Bless The Child' was written in 1939 by Billie Holiday and Arthur Herzog Jr. The song's lyrics were inspired by a fight over money that Holiday had with her mother, in which her mother said, "God bless the child that's got his own." This became the song's hook.

RECOMMENDED LISTENING

The Essential Billie Holiday – The Columbia Years features the original version of 'God Bless The Child' along with a swathe of material from the earliest days of Holiday's career. *Lady Sings The Blues* (1956) has her in good form a few years before her death.

God Bless The Child

Billie Holiday

Words & Music by Billie Holiday & Arthur Herzog Jr.

Ellie Goulding

SONG TITLE: I NEED YOUR LOVE

ALBUM: HALCYON

RELEASED: 2013

LABEL: POLYDOR

GENRE: POP

PERSONNEL: ELLIE GOULDING (VOX)
CALVIN HARRIS (VARIOUS)

UK CHART PEAK: 4
US CHART PEAK: 16

BACKGROUND INFO

'I Need Your Love' was a single by Calvin Harris featuring Ellie Goulding that later featured as a bonus track on Goulding's album *Halcyon*.

THE BIGGER PICTURE

Elena Jane Goulding was born in 1986 in a small village in Herefordshire. She began playing clarinet aged nine then took guitar lessons when she turned 14. Within a year of picking up the guitar she was writing her own folk-inspired songs and later won a singing contest at her college – a promising start. While studying drama at the University of Kent, Goulding discovered electronic music and began to develop her unique sound. Before she could finish her studies, Goulding was discovered by the artist management company Turn First Artists, who insisted she leave university, move to London and focus on her music. She was introduced to the producer Starsmith and the pair began working on the material that would form her debut album, *Lights*. It was a winning combination, as *Lights* debuted at Number 1 on the UK album charts in 2010. Since then Goulding has released an expanded edition of her debut entitled *More Lights* and her second album, *Halcyon*, (another UK chart topper) in 2012.

NOTES

'I Need Your Love' was originally recorded for Scottish DJ/producer Calvin Harris's third studio album *18 Months*. The track was released as a single, labelled 'Calvin Harris featuring Ellie Goulding', on 12 April 2013. It was the seventh single from Harris's album and the seventh to enter the Top 10 of the UK singles chart. The next single from *18 Months*, 'Thinking About You', also went Top 10, making Harris the first artist in British chart history to have eight songs in the Top 10 from one album (the previous record holder was Michael Jackson). Ellie Goulding's record label, keen to cash in on the song's success, included 'I Need Your Love' as a bonus track on a repackaged version of Goulding's album *Halcyon*.

RECOMMENDED LISTENING

Ellie Goulding's cover of Elton John's 'Your Song' has a charm about it that's entirely down to her tender vocal performance. 'Anything Could Happen' is more typical Goulding: heavily effected vocals matched with an uplifting lyric and chord progression. 'Burn' was Goulding's first single to reach Number 1 in the Top 40, with its synth-heavy production and choppy phrasing. 'How Long Will I Love', by contrast, is a piano ballad with vulnerable-sounding vocals.

I Need Your Love

Ellie Goulding

Words & Music by Adam Wiles & Ellie Goulding

SONG TITLE: ROAR
ALBUM: PRISM
RELEASED: 2013
LABEL: CAPITOL
GENRE: POP

PERSONNEL: KATY PERRY (VOX)

UK CHART PEAK: 1
US CHART PEAK: 1

BACKGROUND INFO

'Roar' was the lead single from Katy Perry's fourth album, *Prism*, and a Number 1 hit around the world.

THE BIGGER PICTURE

In 2001 Katy Hudson released her self-titled debut album. She grew up in a religious household and was forbidden from listening to anything other than sacred music, so naturally *Katy Hudson* was a Christian rock record. Shortly after, though, Hudson started working with pop producers who saw her commercial potential – 'Katy Hudson' became 'Katy Perry' and her music turned from praising God to raising eyebrows. Perry's breakthrough single was the controversial 'I Kissed A Girl', featured on her first post-Hudson album, 2008's *One Of The Boys*. It was during the writing of this album that her musical relationship with producer Dr. Luke began. Luke has been responsible for some of the biggest hits of the 21st century, including 'I Kissed A Girl' and 'California Gurls' with Perry, as well as 'Since U Been Gone' (Kelly Clarkson) and 'Wrecking Ball' (Miley Cyrus). It's a relationship that continued through all of Katy Perry's albums up to *Prism*, the record on which Perry got serious, with its themes of failed relationships, living in the present and self-empowerment.

NOTES

Like many pop songs, 'Roar' was written by a team of songwriters. Perry often co-writes with singer-songwriter Bonnie McKee, who is credited as a writer on 'Roar', so the two most likely traded lyric ideas at an early stage of the song's development. The song's producers – Dr. Luke, Max Martin and Cirkut – also get a share of the writing credits and would have written the backing track collaboratively for Perry to sing over. Gottwald and Martin are among pop's most successful writers and there's a good chance they also had some input on the vocal melody (top line) and song arrangement. This process of co-writing is common in pop music and it's not unusual to see even more names listed in a song's credits, especially if another song is sampled and its writers credited too.

RECOMMENDED LISTENING

Katy Perry's breakthrough single, 'I Kissed A Girl', was an early highlight with its swaggering rock riffing, unforgettable vocal hooks and racy lyrics. 'Last Friday Night (T.G.I.F.)', from 2010's *Teenage Dream* went even further lyrically with its tales of debauchery and cheeky music video. 'Firework', from the same album, shows a more emotional, less tongue-in-cheek side to Perry and a powerful vocal performance.

Roar

Katy Perry

Words & Music by Katy Perry, Lukasz Gottwald,
Bonnie McKee, Max Martin
& Henry Russell Walter

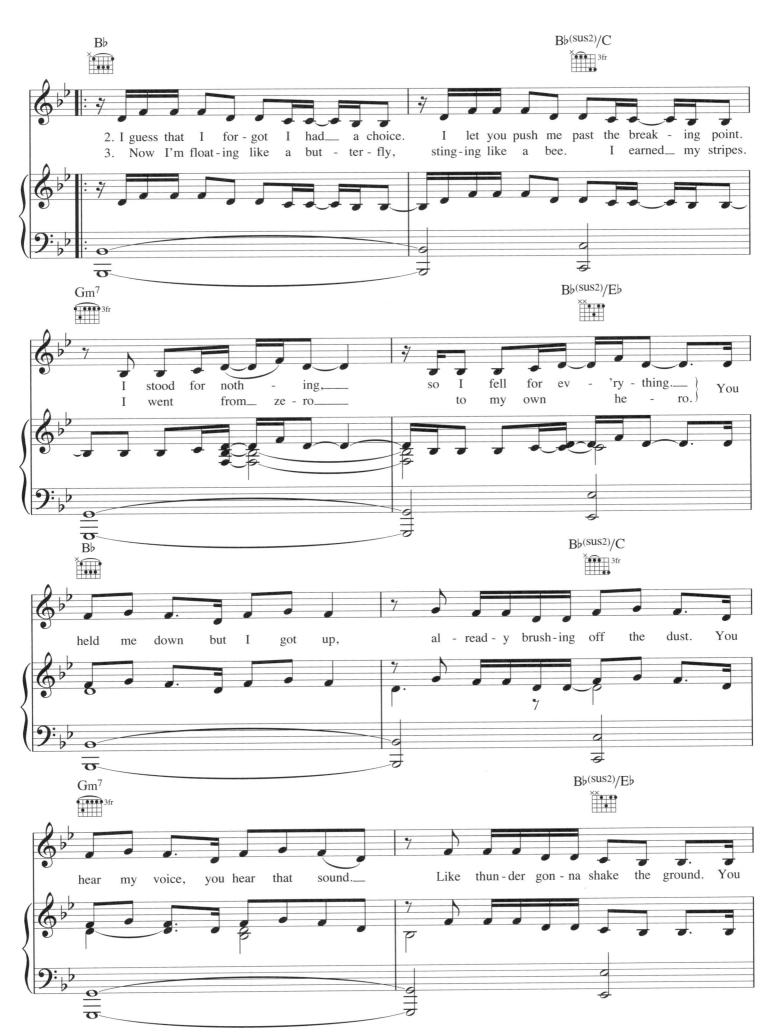

SONG TITLE: WALKING ON SUNSHINE
ALBUM: WALKING ON SUNSHINE
RELEASED: 1985
LABEL: CAPITOL RECORDS
GENRE: POP ROCK

PERSONNEL: KATRINA LESKANICH (VOX)
KIMBERLEY REW (GUITAR)
VINCE DE LA CRUZ (BASS)
ALEX COOPER (DRUMS)

UK CHART PEAK: 8
US CHART PEAK: 9

BACKGROUND INFO

'Walking On Sunshine' was the breakthrough single for the UK-based pop rock group Katrina And The Waves, after years on the covers circuit.

THE BIGGER PICTURE

The roots of Katrina And The Waves go back to 1975, when guitarist Kimberly Rew and drummer Alex Cooper formed a group called The Waves. For two years they played in and around their home town of Cambridge before Rew left to join a group called The Soft Boys. The Waves carried on after Rew's departure until 1979, when Cooper also left to join a covers band called Mama's Cookin', featuring American singer Katrina Leskanich. Mama's Cookin' played England's US military bases (a rite of passage for many bands at the time) performing soul, pop, R&B and seventies rock. Then, in 1981, The Soft Boys split up and Alex Cooper persuaded Kimberley Rew to join Mama's Cookin', which was renamed The Waves after Cooper and Rew's first group. Initially, Rew was the lead singer and the group's sole songwriter as they added more original songs to their set. However, Rew saw potential in Leskanich and made her the lead singer, renaming the band for the final time, 'Katrina And The Waves'.

NOTES

Success didn't come quickly for Katrina And The Waves. Although Rew's knack for writing catchy, guitar-driven pop seemed tailor-made for the charts, only a small independent record label, Attic Records, had the faith to sign the band. And even then, K&TW's records were only released in Canada. Nevertheless, this exposure led to one of Rew's songs, 'Going Down To Liverpool', being chosen for The Bangles' debut album, which in turn led to the major labels at last becoming interested in Katrina And The Waves. Capitol Records signed the band and released its self-titled debut album worldwide in 1985. It went Top 30 in the UK and US, and K&TW were nominated in the Grammys' 'Best Band' category. The album's lead single, 'Walking On Sunshine', went Top 10 on both sides of the Atlantic.

RECOMMENDED LISTENING

Before it was a hit for The Bangles, 'Going Down To Liverpool' was one of many songs written by Kimberley Rew for Katrina And The Waves. The group had a late career revival when they represented the UK in the Eurovision Song Contest with Rew's 'Love Shine A Light' – and won. The song was a Top 10 hit across Europe.

Female Vocals Grade 1

Walking On Sunshine

Katrina & The Waves
Words & Music by Kimberley Rew

Female Vocals Grade 1

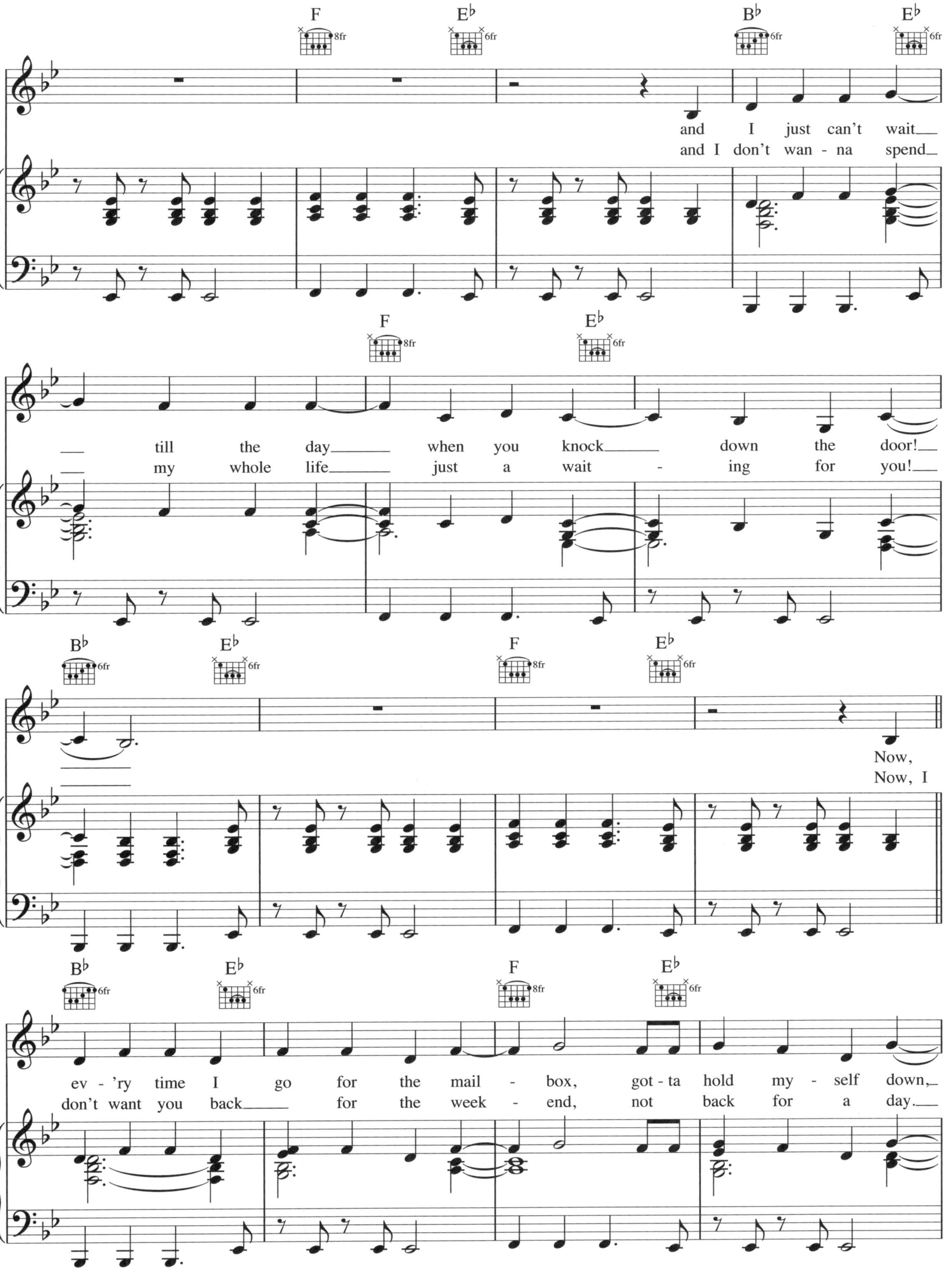

'cause
I said,

I just can't wait____ till you write____ me you're com ‑ ing a ‑ round.____
ba ‑ by I just____ want you back,____ and I want____ you to stay.____

I'm walk ‑ ing on____ sun ‑

§ Dm/F   E♭

‑ shine,_____ whoa._____ I'm walk ‑ ing on____ sun ‑

SONG TITLE: SOMEWHERE ONLY WE KNOW
ALBUM: SHEEZUS
RELEASED: 2013
LABEL: PARLOPHONE
GENRE: POP

PERSONNEL: LILY ALLEN (VOX)
PAUL BEARD (PIANO)
PAUL SAYER (GUITAR)

UK CHART PEAK: 1
US CHART PEAK: N/A

BACKGROUND INFO

'Somewhere Only We Know' was Lily Allen's third Number 1 single in the UK. It is a cover of a song by the rock group Keane.

THE BIGGER PICTURE

Lily Rose Beatrice Allen was born in London in 1985. She is the daughter of actor Keith Allen and film producer Alison Owen. Allen's parents split up when she was four, which may have had an influence on her behaviour at school – she was expelled from several schools for a range of wrongdoings. In spite of this, Allen was a keen student of music, taking singing lessons and playing piano, violin, guitar and trumpet. She dropped out of school aged 15, went on holiday to Ibiza and ended up staying on, working in a record shop but again living a far from virtuous lifestyle. Fortunately, she was discovered by A&R man George Lamb, who rescued her and took her on as his client. Allen signed her first record deal in 2002, but her label, London Records, lost interest and nothing was released. Lily persevered and in 2005 signed to a subsidiary of Parlophone records. The singer's success was largely down to her posting songs she recorded for the label on her MySpace page, which created a buzz on social media prior to any records being released officially. Her debut album, *Alright, Still* (2006), went Top 40 in 13 countries and suddenly Allen was a media sensation, known for her risqué persona and outspokenness. In 2009, her second album, *It's Not Me, It's You*, was an even bigger success, topping the UK albums chart. *Sheezus* followed in 2014 and also went to Number 1.

NOTES

'Somewhere Only We Know' was originally written and recorded by the English piano rock group Keane, and released in 2004. Lily Allen's version was made available for digital download before the release of her third album, *Sheezus*. It also featured in John Lewis's Christmas television ad, which had already proved lucrative for several singers before Allen.

RECOMMENDED LISTENING

'Smile' and 'LDN' were Top 10 hits from Lily Allen's debut album, *Alright, Still*, and are representative of her early sound – cutesy pop with an edge. 'The Fear' and 'Not Fair' are standout tracks from her second album, *It's Not Me, It's You*, while 'Hard Out Here', the first single from *Sheezus*, was a continuation of the Lily Allen sound and attitude.

Somewhere Only We Know

Lily Allen

Words & Music by Richard Hughes, Tim Rice-Oxley & Tom Chaplin

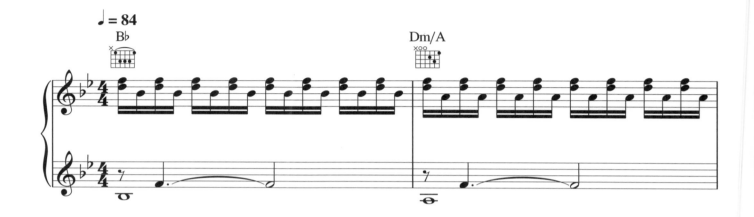

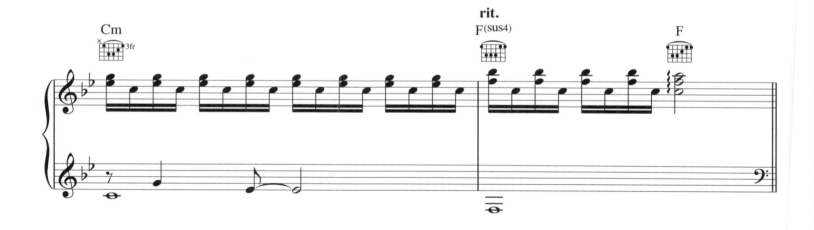

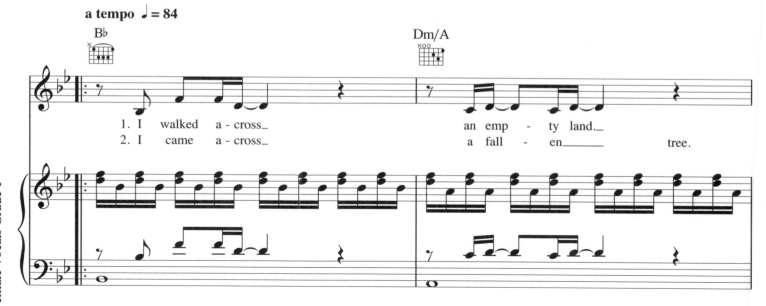

1. I walked a-cross_ an emp - ty land._

2. I came a-cross_ a fall - en_ tree.

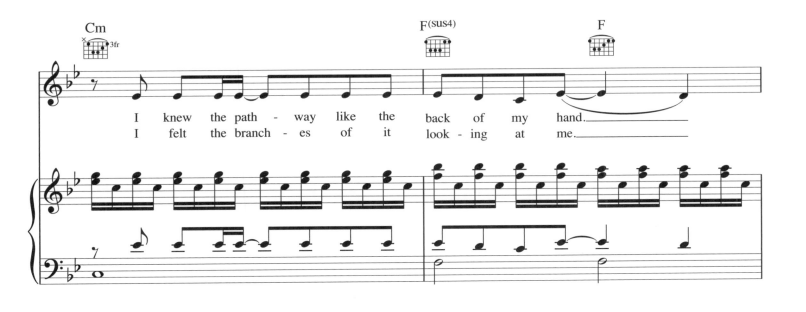

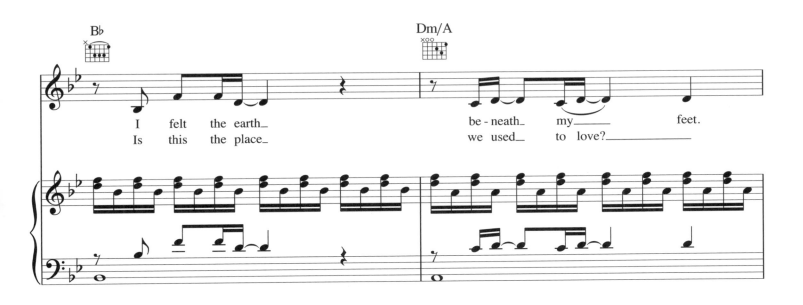

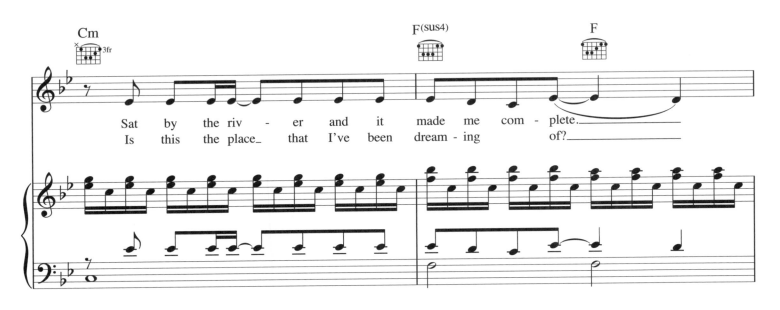

end of ev - 'ry - thing.___ So why don't we___ go. some - where on - ly we

know.

Some - where on - ly we know.___

a tempo ♩ = 84

(Ah,

ah.

Con pedale

Ah,_____ ah.

Technical Exercises

Group A: Scales

The major scale should be prepared as shown below. You may select any starting note from A–E. You will be asked if you would like to sing along to a metronome click or hear four clicks before you start. Whichever option you choose, you will hear your chosen starting note before the count starts. You may perform this test using any vocal sound except humming or whistling. The tempo is ♩=70.

Group B: Arpeggios

In this group, both of the arpeggio exercises need to be prepared as shown below. You will be asked to perform one of them in the exam, as chosen by the examiner.

This test is performed to a metronome click track and you may select any starting note from A–E. You will hear the root note followed by a one-bar (three or four click) count-in. You may perform this test using any vocal sound except humming or whistling. The tempo is ♩=70.

A major arpeggio | Pattern 1

A major arpeggio | Pattern 2

Group C: Intervals

In this group, both the major 2nd and major 3rd intervals need to be prepared as below. You will be asked to perform one of them in the exam, as chosen by the examiner.

The examiner will choose a starting note within the range A–C. You will hear this note followed by a four-beat count-in. You may perform this test using any vocal sound except humming or whistling. The tempo is ♩=90.

Major 2nd interval

Major 3rd interval

Group D: Technical Studies

This group consists of two Technical Studies: one rhythmic and one melodic. The examiner will ask you to perform one in the exam. The examiner will decide which, so you must prepare *both* before the exam. The rhythmic test starts with a four-beat count. The melodic test starts with a root note followed by a four-beat count. Both tests should be performed to the appropriate backing track which can be found on the download card.

1. Rhythmic | Rhythmic accuracy

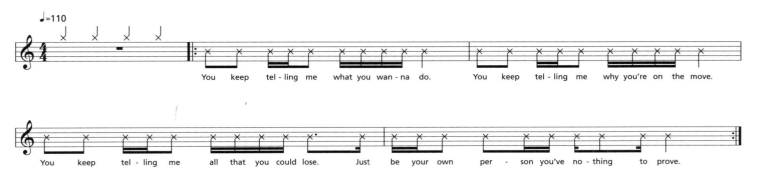

2. Melodic | Dynamic change

Sight Reading

In this section you have a choice between:

- *Either* – a sight reading test
- *Or* – an improvisation and interpretation test (see facing page).

The examiner will ask you which one you wish to choose before commencing. Once you have decided, you cannot change your mind.

The examiner will give you a four-bar melody in the key of C major covering a range up to a major 3rd. You will be given 90 seconds to practise, after which you will perform the test. The tempo is ♩=70.

During the practise time you will be given the choice of a metronome click throughout or a count-in of four beats at the beginning. Whichever option you choose, the practise time will start with the examiner playing the root note. You will receive the same choice when performing the test. The test will start with the root note.

You may perform this test using any vocal sound except humming or whistling.

Please note: the test shown is an example. The examiner will give you a different version in the exam.

Improvisation & Interpretation

The examiner will give you a chord sequence in the key of C major. You must improvise a melody over the backing track. You will hear the backing track three times. The first and second time is for you to rehearse and the third time is for you to perform the final version for the exam. Each playthrough will begin with the root note and a four-beat count-in. The backing track is continuous throughout, so once the first playthrough has finished, the root note and count-in of the second and third playthroughs will start immediately. The tempo is ♩=70–80.

You may perform this test using any vocal sound except humming or whistling.

Please note: the test shown is an example. The examiner will give you a different version in the exam.

Ear Tests

In this section, there are two ear tests:
- Melodic Recall
- Rhythmic Recall

You will find one example of each type of test printed below and you will be given both of them in the exam.

Test 1 | Melodic Recall

The examiner will play you three consecutive notes. You will need to identify whether the last two notes are higher or lower in sequence. This means you will need to tell the examiner whether the second note is higher or lower than the first, and whether the third note is higher or lower than the second. You will hear the test twice, each time with a four-beat *vocal* count-in. The tempo is ♩=85.

Please use the words 'higher', 'lower', 'up' or 'down' in your answer.

Please note: the test shown is an example. The examiner will give you a different version in the exam.

Test 2 | Rhythmic Recall

This test comes in two parts:

Part 1 | Rhythmic Recall

The examiner will play you a two-bar rhythm played on a single note to a drum backing. You will hear the test twice. Each time the test is played it is preceded by a four-beat count-in. There will be a short gap for you to practise after each playthrough. Next you will hear a *vocal* count-in, after which you should sing the rhythm back. The tempo is ♩=90.

For this exercise, use 'da' or 'ba' vocal sounds.

It is acceptable to sing over the track as it is being played as well as practising after the first two playthroughs. The length of time available after the second playthrough is pre-recorded on the audio track so the vocal count-in may begin while you are still practising.

Part 2 | Identification

You will then be asked to identify the rhythm heard in part 1 from two printed examples shown to you by the examiner.

Please note: the test shown is an example. The examiner will give you a different version in the exam.

General Musicianship Questions

In this part of the exam you will be asked five questions. Four of these will be about general music knowledge and the fifth will be about your voice.

Part 1 | General Music Knowledge

The examiner will ask four music knowledge questions from the categories below. The questions will be based on one of the pieces (including Free Choice Pieces) performed by you in the exam. You can choose which one.

If there are handwritten notes on the piece you have chosen, the examiner may ask you to choose an alternative.

You will be *asked to identify:*
- The treble clef.
- The time signature.
- Whole-, half-, quarter- and eighth-note values.
- A rest in the piece.

Part 2 | Your Voice

The examiner will also ask you one question about your voice. Brief demonstrations to assist your answer are acceptable.

You will be asked:
- Where is your diaphragm?
- Where is your larynx?
- What is the difference between head voice and chest voice?
- Why is it important to warm up before singing?

Entering Exams, Exam Procedure & Marking Schemes

Entering Exams

Entering a Rockschool exam is easy. You can enter online at *www.rockschool.co.uk* or by downloading and filling in an exam entry form. The full Rockschool examination terms and conditions as well as exam periods and current fees are available from our website or by calling +44 (0)845 460 4747.

Exam procedure

In the exam you can decide whether to start with the Performance Pieces or the Technical Exercises. These will be followed by the Supporting Tests (Ear Tests and Quick Study Pieces) and General Musicianship Questions.

Use Of Microphone

At Level 1 (Grades 1–3) microphone use is optional, although candidates may use one if they feel it will enhance their performance. At Level 2 (Grades 4–5) microphone use is obligatory for all pieces and at Level 3 (Grades 6–8) for the whole exam.

Marking Schemes

Below are the marking schemes for the two different types of Rockschool exam.

GRADE EXAMS | GRADES 1–5

ELEMENT	PASS	MERIT	DISTINCTION
Performance Piece 1	12–14 out of 20	15–17 out of 20	18+ out of 20
Performance Piece 2	12–14 out of 20	15–17 out of 20	18+ out of 20
Performance Piece 3	12–14 out of 20	15–17 out of 20	18+ out of 20
Technical Exercises	9–10 out of 15	11–12 out of 15	13+ out of 15
Either Sight Reading *or* Improvisation & Interpretation	6 out of 10	7–8 out of 10	9+ out of 10
Ear Tests	6 out of 10	7–8 out of 10	9+ out of 10
General Musicianship Questions	3 out of 5	4 out of 5	5 out of 5
TOTAL MARKS	60%+	74%+	90%+

PERFORMANCE CERTIFICATES | GRADES 1–8

ELEMENT	PASS	MERIT	DISTINCTION
Performance Piece 1	12–14 out of 20	15–17 out of 20	18+ out of 20
Performance Piece 2	12–14 out of 20	15–17 out of 20	18+ out of 20
Performance Piece 3	12–14 out of 20	15–17 out of 20	18+ out of 20
Performance Piece 4	12–14 out of 20	15–17 out of 20	18+ out of 20
Performance Piece 5	12–14 out of 20	15–17 out of 20	18+ out of 20
TOTAL MARKS	60%+	75%+	90%+

Female Vocals Grade 1

Improvisation Requirements & Free Choice Pieces

At Rockschool it is our aim to encourage creativity and individualism. We therefore give candidates the opportunity to express themselves musically within styles of their own choice. For this reason, Free Choice Pieces are accepted in all Vocals grades. In addition, all songs performed in exams from Grade 3 onwards have compulsory improvisation requirements.

Improvisation Requirements

From Grade 3, all songs, whether from the grade book or chosen as FCPs, need to incorporate improvisation. The improvisation can be prepared in advance, but is expected to be individually constructed, and needs to include **both** vocal ad-libbing and re-working of existing melody lines as follows:

Level 1 Grade 3:	Vocal ad-libbing (2–4 bars) and re-working of melody line (4 bars)
Level 2 Grades 4–5:	Vocal ad-libbing (4–8 bars) and re-working of melody line (4–8 bars)
Level 3 Grades 6–7:	Vocal ad-libbing (8–12 bars) and re-working of melody line (8 bars)
Level 3 Grades 8:	Vocal ad-libbing (12–16 bars) and re-working of melody line (8 bars)

For all pieces, you will need to highlight the sheet music to show the examiner the location of both ad-libbed and re-worked parts at the beginning of the exam.

Notes

- You are free to choose where you improvise. However, in all cases, improvisations need to be a continuous number of bars, not a number of smaller bars which in total add up to the ranges shown.

- Vocal ad-lib could be demonstrated in, for example, introductions, endings or open instrumental parts.

- Re-working of a melody could be demonstrated by altering any existing singing parts; for example, verses, choruses, bridges.

- For both ad-lib and re-working of a melody, you need to demonstrate an awareness of harmony, melody, phrasing, use of rhythms and incorporation of any appropriate expression in a stylistically appropriate manner. Range and content will be expected to increase progressively as you move through the grades.

- We would encourage re-working to take place later in a piece after the original has been presented to show you can portray the original, then you are able to adapt appropriately with individual colour.

- Improvisation can be a good place to demonstrate your head voice, which can often be omitted, reducing the technical content of a piece at a particular grade.

Free Choice Pieces (FCPs)

An FCP is defined as any piece outside the grade book, and can fall into two categories:

1) **Wider Repertoire:** a full list of pre-approved and regularly updated pieces can be found on *www.rockschool.co.uk*. These songs can be used **without** prior approval from Rockschool.

2) **Own Choice:** candidates can choose any song in any genre outside the grade book and wider repertoire. These songs can, however, only be used **with** prior approval from Rockschool. This requirement is compulsory and you need to contact the office to have your chosen piece(s) approved. Please allow five weeks before your exam to receive a decision.

We cannot accept any songs which have not been approved or are not contained in the grade book or wider repertoire.

For all grades, candidates can choose the following number of FCPs in the exam:

Grade Examinations:	Up to 2 of 3 pieces can be free choice. (At least one piece must be from the grade book.)
Performance Certificates:	Up to 3 of 5 pieces can be free choice. (At least two pieces must be from the grade book.)

For all FCPs, candidates will need to bring the sheet music and a backing track (without vocal part) on the day. A memory stick, iPod or CD/DVD is acceptable and we would also suggest a second source to be safe. It will not be necessary to bring the sheet music or backing tracks for pieces chosen from the grade book.

Copyright Information

1234
(Feist/Seltmann)
Kobalt Music Publishing Limited/Universal Music Publishing MGB Limited

God Bless The Child
(Holiday/Herzog)
Carlin Music Corporation

I Need Your Love
(Wiles/Goulding)
EMI Music Publishing Limited/Global Talent Publishing

Roar
(Perry/Gottwald/McKee/Max/Walter)
Kobalt Music Publishing Limited/Warner/Chappell North America Limited/Kassner Associated Music Publishers Limited

Walking On Sunshine
(Rew)
Touch Tones Music Limited

Somewhere Only We Know
(Hughes/Rice-Oxley/Chaplin)
Universal Music Publishing MGB Limited

mcps